YOUR COMPUTER THINKS YOU'RE AN IDIOT!

by RANDY GLASBERGEN

CCC PUBLICATIONS, LLC

Published by

CCC Publications
9725 Lurline Avenue
Chatsworth, CA 91311

Manufactured in the United States of America

Cover © 2000 CCC Publications

Interior illustrations © 2000 CCC Publications

Cover & interior art by Randy Glasbergen

Cover production by Continental Imaging Center, Chatsworth, CA

ISBN: 1-57644-121-0

If your local U.S. bookstore is out of stock, copies of this book may be obtained by mailing check or money order for $7.95 per book (plus $3.00 to cover postage and handling) to:
CCC Publications; 9725 Lurline Avenue; Chatsworth, CA 91311.

Pre-publication Edition - 01/01

INTRODUCTION

If your laptop is the only warm thing you've ever held on your lap . . .
YOUR COMPUTER THINKS YOU'RE AN IDIOT!

If your cat has her own e-mail address and gets more letters than you . . .
YOUR COMPUTER THINKS YOU'RE AN IDIOT!

If you spent $3000 at the computer store just so you could download fruitcake recipes . . .
YOUR COMPUTER THINKS YOU'RE AN IDIOT!

If you've ever used an online auction to bid on celebrity toenail clippings . . .
YOUR COMPUTER THINKS YOU'RE AN IDIOT!

If you're not as pathetic as the pople in these cartoons,
maybe your computer has misjudged you . . .
BUT STILL THINKS YOU'RE AN IDIOT ANYWAY!

ABOUT THE AUTHOR

Since putting his cartoons on the Internet in 1995, **RANDY GLASBERGEN** has become one of the world's most popular cartoonists. His cartoons appear worldwide in magazines, newspapers, calendars, greeting cards; on coffee mugs, mouse pads, screen savers, and CD-ROMs. He is also the creator of the syndicated comic strip, THE BETTER HALF, and author of several cartooning instruction books. His computer also thinks he's an idiot!

For more Randy Glasbergen cartoons, visit: **www.glasbergen.com**

"We couldn't afford faster computers,
so we just made them *sound* faster."

"Either you learn to do it MY way or you go back to the computer store!"

"The screen is all shaky----even when I shop online, I get the cart with the wobbly wheels!"

When Techies Dream.

"NEVER HIT THE SAME KEY OVER AND OVER...THEY HATE THAT!"

"My family changed the password and locked me out of the computer. They caught me downloading tofu recipes."

"There aren't any icons to click. It's a chalk board."

"You'll give your credit card to a waitress with sixteen earrings and an obscene tattoo, but you won't give it a reputable company with a web site?"

"IT'S A NONVIOLENT ACTION GAME. WHEN A NINJA ATTACKS YOU, YOUR GOAL IS TO IDENTIFY THE SOURCE OF HIS HOSTILITY AND FIND HIM A THERAPIST."

"Your computer claims you touched it
in an inappropriate manner."

Why Very Few Supermodels Own Computers.

"I'm looking up some important stuff:
Does tail wagging count as aerobic exercise?
How long should you know someone before
you lick their face? What do the etiquette
rules say about drinking from the toilet?"

"IS IT JUST MY IMAGINATION, OR DOES OUR COMPUTER SEEM AWFULLY COCKY SINCE IT SURVIVED THAT Y2K THING?"

"HAVE YOU EVER NOTICED THAT WE NEVER NEED TO UPGRADE TO A FASTER REFRIGERATOR, GET A NEW OPERATING SYSTEM FOR OUR STOVE, OR BUY A BUNCH OF TOASTER ADD-ONS?"

"ARE YOU TRYING TO AUCTION YOUR BRUSSELS SPROUTS AGAIN?"

"Your machine can't put me on hold,
I am a very important business executive!
I demand to be ignored by a real person!"

"MY DAD DOESN'T KNOW A LOT ABOUT COMPUTERS.
HE THINKS ISDN AND MP3 WERE THE ROBOTS ON 'STAR WARS'."

Computer Shack

"I need a 750 MHz processor, voice recognition technology, ISDN networking capability, DVD-ROM and CD-RW, earth-shaking stereo speakers, and a blistering kick-butt graphics card to help me organize my recipe files."

"Our computers at work are so old, you have to type in every command...in Morse Code!"

SOFTWARE

"I NEED A BETTER WORD PROCESSOR FOR MY HUSBAND.
ONE THAT WILL CORRECT HIS SPELLING, GRAMMAR AND OPINIONS."

"Do you, Jason, take Heather to have and to hold,
to e-mail and to fax, to page and to beep,
until death do you part?"

"I've discovered the secret to successful online investing. If you hold down Ctrl + Alt + Shift, while pressing the arrow key, your stocks go up!"

"Five years ago, my husband and I fell in love over the Internet. To celebrate our anniversary, we're finally going to meet face to face!"

Computer Technical Support Hotline

"We're not getting anywhere, Mr. Johnson.
Can I have a word with your computer in private?"

"Our online investments are growing too slowly.
We need to get a faster computer!"

"I HACKED INTO THE SCHOOL'S COMPUTER AND CHANGED ALL MY GRADES. THEN THE SCHOOL HACKED INTO MY COMPUTER AND DELETED ALL MY GAMES!"

"I SET UP THE COMPUTER TO CONTROL ALL OF OUR HOUSEHOLD APPLIANCES, BUT I'M NOT SURE WHY WE'RE GETTING E-MAIL ON OUR TOAST."

Exchange Student From Silicon Valley.

"I just want a few minutes of quiet time—
LEAVE ME ALONE!!!!!!!!!!!!"

"If YOU want to fly coast to coast for 75 cents, that's fine. But I'd feel safer paying full price!"

"Our best palm-size computer comes with many portable peripherals, including the nose-top printer, a scanner hat, and 100MB removable storage socks!"

"You can correct my spelling and grammar,
but my ethics are none of your business!"

"IF YOU WANT TO KNOW THE MEANING OF LIFE, GO TO MY WEB PAGE AND TYPE IN YOUR CREDIT CARD NUMBER."

"IF I CAN HACK INTO MOTHER NATURE'S COMPUTER, WE'RE LOOKING AT NINE MORE MONTHS OF WINTER!"

"IT'S NOT A NICOTINE PATCH, IT'S A CD-ROM.
I'M TRYING TO OVERCOME COMPUTER ADDICTION."

"THANK YOU FOR CALLING TECHNICAL SUPPORT. THIS CALL MAY BE MONITORED SO WE CAN PLAY IT BACK AT COMPANY PARTIES FOR LAUGHS."

"DON'T USE YOUR COMPUTER TO HELP YOU SHOP
FOR A NEW COMPUTER -- YOU'LL HURT ITS FEELINGS!"

"The best thing about my Palm Pilot?
Most people never notice it's a Game Boy!"

"Until the computer is back in service,
everything that goes wrong should
be blamed on the copier."

"Hello, technical support?"

"ON AUGUST 9, 1556 NOSTRADAMUS PREDICTED THE COMING OF COMPUTERS AND THE INTERNET. THAT SAME NIGHT, HE AND HIS WIFE HAD THE VERY FIRST MAC VS. PC ARGUMENT."

"WHEN DID THE COMPUTER START WRITING ITSELF A PAYCHECK?"

"Today at work, I received 650 E-mails from feedme@homecat.com! Was that *you*?"

"Unless you meet my list of demands by midnight tonight, I'm going to post your old yearbook picture on the Internet."

"ANYONE CAUGHT USING OFFICE COMPUTERS FOR PERSONAL BUSINESS WILL BE DEALT WITH SWIFTLY AND APPROPRIATELY."

"No, I don't think you're crazy. Like most of us, you're just a victim of bad programming."

"A hacker broke into our computer,
tuned up our hard drive, balanced our checkbook,
updated our software and left us a bill for $200."

"KEEP YOUR FACE PRESSED AGAINST THE SCREEN. I'LL RUN PHOTOSHOP AND SEE IF I CAN RETOUCH YOUR FACE TO LOOK AS GOOD AS YOUR SENIOR PORTRAIT."

"The microphone is so you can go to Internet chat rooms and bark at strangers."

"You invested $100 a week ago and we're not rich yet.
I thought you knew how to use a computer!"

"It's the latest innovation in office safety.
When your computer crashes, an air bag is activated
so you won't bang your head in frustration."

"What button do I push to change
the size of my cursor?"

The Downside of Voice Recognition Software.

"IF YOU MISS ME WHEN I GO AWAY TO COLLEGE, JUST VISIT MY WEB PAGE AND CLICK THE AUDIO FILE TO HEAR ME YELL AT YOU."

"THERE'S NOTHING IN THE MANUAL THAT SAYS I CAN'T
USE THE CD-ROM LASER TO HEAT UP AN ENGLISH MUFFIN!"

"Dear Mom and Dad...How have you been?
I am fine. I miss you. If my hard drive
ever crashes, I will come downstairs to visit
you sometime. PS: Please e-mail me some food."

"Debbie, when you tried to upload your little brother to Timbuktu, did you jam him into the disk drive nose first or feet first?"

"He didn't fall in love with someone on the computer. He fell in love with the computer!"

"GO ASK YOUR MOTHER. AND IF SHE'S BUSY, GO ASK THE INTERNET."

"IF OUR COMPUTER IS SO SMART, HOW COME IT'S THE ONLY APPLIANCE IN OUR HOUSE THAT REQUIRES 24-HOUR TECHNICAL SUPPORT?"

The Truth About Y2K.

"My mom got me this game. Every time you blow up an alien, you have to stop and clean up the mess before you can continue to play."

"This is a story about Rip Van Winkle,
a man who called tech support and
was put on hold for 100 years!"

Computer Repairs

"Most laptops are pretty well behaved,
but once in a while you get one that bites."

"I'M TIRED OF ARGUING WITH MY SPELL CHECKER! FROM NOW ON, YOUR NAME IS 'KETTLE BOWLER' NOT 'KENNETH FOWLER'."

"THE COMPUTER SAYS I NEED TO UPGRADE MY BRAIN
TO BE COMPATIBLE WITH ITS NEW SOFTWARE."

"Do you MIND?!"

"TRY WWW.COURAGE.COM"

BURP!

GLASBERGEN

HOW TO TELL WHEN YOUR HARD DRIVE IS GETTING TOO FULL.

"No, it's not the baby's web page."

"I found five dollars and I'm going to invest it.
As soon as it grows to $500, I'm going to buy my
own sofa and nobody can tell me to stay off it!"

"How many times have I warned you?
Never stick your tongue on a frozen computer screen!"

"CAN'T YOU JUST GO 'BEEP' LIKE MY OLD SPELL CHECKER?"

"I received an e-mail with an audio file attachment.
I think my cat wants to be fed."

"The toaster pastry fits right into the floppy drive!
This allows you to transfer data from your computer
to your mouth. The information is stored in your
fat cells, thus transforming your pot belly
into a high-capacity hard drive!"

"I CAN'T FIND A GOOD PHOTO FOR MY WEB PAGE.
EVERY PICTURE OF ME LOOKS TOO MUCH LIKE ME!"

"WE DON'T HAVE THREE DOLLARS TO RENT A DVD,
SO WE'RE WATCHING A SLICE OF BOLOGNA."

"I've received a number of complaints from your computer. You haven't been washing your hands after you go to the toilet."

"Ever have one of those days when one millionth of a nanosecond feels like an eternity?"

"Our latest chip contains Ginkgo Biloba to help improve your computer's memory and mental focus!"

"I'M A HUMANITARIAN HACKER. MY GOAL IS TO REMOVE ALL TOFU RECIPES FROM THE INTERNET!"

"I HAVE TO FIX SOMETHING. MY LITTLE BROTHER
SOLD MY PARENTS ON E-BAY."

"I THINK MY REPORT MIGHT BE TOO BORING.
MY COMPUTER KEEPS GOING INTO SLEEP MODE."

"I'm sending you to a seminar to help you work harder and be more productive."

"Information security is becoming a big problem here. Do you still have my Captain Crunch decoder ring, Ma?"

"NORMALLY, I GET ALONG GREAT WITH EVERYONE,
BUT MY SPELL CHECKER AND I CAN'T AGREE ON *ANYTHING!*"

"According to encyclopedia, we should have grown legs and evolved into land creatures millions of years ago. Why didn't we get a memo about this?!"

"I'd like to upgrade from a cheeseburger to a high-capacity bacon cheeseburger with 10 megabytes of pickles and onions. And we'll be sharing an order of fries, so make sure they're hot-swapable."

"He's dot-com and I'm dot-net, but we've decided to raise the children as dot-org."

"Our competition launched their web site, stole all of our customers and put us out of business while you were in the john."

"I'M THE COMPUTER FAIRY. TECHNICAL SUPPORT SENDS ME TO FIX THE WORST PROBLEMS."

"Getting married is like buying a computer. Even if you're very careful to pick one that's perfect for all of your needs, in a few months all you'll do is complain."

"They've made online shopping so much like the real thing, after visiting 20 stores I'm exhausted and my feet hurt!"

"You need to get a better password.
MEOW was way too easy to guess!"

"The computer has made it much easier to invest my money. First I invested in a larger monitor, then I invested in a faster hard drive, then I invested in a better keyboard, then I...."

"You can correct my spelling and grammar,
but stop trying to spice up my love letters!"

"I like my digital signature just the way it is—
stop dotting my 'i' with a little flower!"

"Any time you're in danger and need help,
just visit my web site for hundreds of crime-fighting
tips plus official t-shirts, mugs, and mouse pads!"

"WHEN HE YELLS AT YOU AND CALLS YOU
BAD NAMES, HOW DOES THAT MAKE YOU FEEL?"

"It's not an encrypted message...
the boss is just a really bad speller."

TITLES BY CCC PUBLICATIONS

Blank Books ($3.99)
GUIDE TO SEX AFTER BABY
GUIDE TO SEX AFTER 30
GUIDE TO SEX AFTER 40
GUIDE TO SEX AFTER 50
GUIDE TO SEX AFTER MARRIAGE

Retail $4.95 – $4.99
"?" book
LAST DIET BOOK YOU'LL EVER NEED
CAN SEX IMPROVE YOUR GOLF?
THE COMPLETE BOOGER BOOK
FLYING FUNNIES
MARITAL BLISS & OXYMORONS
THE ADULT DOT-TO-DOT BOOK
THE DEFINITIVE FART BOOK
THE COMPLETE WIMP'S GUIDE TO SEX
THE CAT OWNER'S SHAPE UP MANUAL
THE OFFICE FROM HELL
FITNESS FANATICS
YOUNGER MEN ARE BETTER THAN RETIN-A
BUT OSSIFER, IT'S NOT MY FAULT
YOU KNOW YOU'RE AN OLD FART WHEN...
1001 WAYS TO PROCRASTINATE
HORMONES FROM HELL II
SHARING THE ROAD WITH IDIOTS
THE GREATEST ANSWERING MACHINE MESSAGES
WHAT DO WE DO NOW??
HOW TO TALK YOU WAY OUT OF A TRAFFIC TICKET
THE BOTTOM HALF
LIFE'S MOST EMBARRASSING MOMENTS
HOW TO ENTERTAIN PEOPLE YOU HATE
YOUR GUIDE TO CORPORATE SURVIVAL
NO HANG-UPS (Volumes I, II & III – $3.95 ea.)
TOTALLY OUTRAGEOUS BUMPER-SNICKERS ($2.95)

Retail $5.95
30 – DEAL WITH IT!
40 – DEAL WITH IT!
50 – DEAL WITH IT!
60 – DEAL WITH IT!
OVER THE HILL – DEAL WITH IT!
SLICK EXCUSES FOR STUPID SCREW-UPS
SINGLE WOMEN VS. MARRIED WOMEN
TAKE A WOMAN'S WORD FOR IT
SEXY CROSSWORD PUZZLES
SO, YOU'RE GETTING MARRIED
YOU KNOW HE'S A WOMANIZING SLIMEBALL WHEN...
GETTING OLD SUCKS
WHY GOD MAKES BALD GUYS
OH BABY!
PMS CRAZED: TOUCH ME AND I'LL KILL YOU!
WHY MEN ARE CLUELESS
THE BOOK OF WHITE TRASH
THE ART OF MOONING
GOLFAHOLICS
CRINKLED 'N' WRINKLED
SMART COMEBACKS FOR STUPID QUESTIONS
YIKES! IT'S ANOTHER BIRTHDAY
SEX IS A GAME
SEX AND YOUR STARS
SIGNS YOUR SEX LIFE IS DEAD
MALE BASHING: WOMEN'S FAVORITE PASTIME
THINGS YOU CAN DO WITH A USELESS MAN
MORE THINGS YOU CAN DO WITH A USELESS MAN
RETIREMENT: THE GET EVEN YEARS
LITTLE INSTRUCTION BOOK OF THE RICH & FAMOUS
WELCOME TO YOUR MIDLIFE CRISIS
GETTING EVEN WITH THE ANSWERING MACHINE
ARE YOU A SPORTS NUT?
MEN ARE PIGS / WOMEN ARE BITCHES
THE BETTER HALF
ARE WE DYSFUNCTIONAL YET?
TECHNOLOGY BYTES!
50 WAYS TO HUSTLE YOUR FRIENDS
HORMONES FROM HELL
HUSBANDS FROM HELL
KILLER BRAS & Other Hazards Of The 50's
IT'S BETTER TO BE OVER THE HILL THAN UNDER IT

HOW TO REALLY PARTY!!!
WORK SUCKS!
THE PEOPLE WATCHER'S FIELD GUIDE
THE ABSOLUTE LAST CHANCE DIET BOOK
THE UGLY TRUTH ABOUT MEN
NEVER A DULL CARD
THE LITTLE BOOK OF ROMANTIC LIES

Retail $6.95
EVERYTHING I KNOW I LEARNED FROM TRASH TALK TV
IN A PERFECT WORLD
I WISH I DIDN'T...
THE TOILET ZONE
SIGNS/TOO MUCH TIME W/CAT
LOVE & MARRIAGE & DIVORCE
CYBERGEEK IS CHIC
THE DIFFERENCE BETWEEN MEN AND WOMEN
GO TO HEALTH!
NOT TONIGHT, DEAR, I HAVE A COMPUTER!
THINGS YOU WILL NEVER HEAR THEM SAY
THE SENIOR CITIZENS'S SURVIVAL GUIDE
IT'S A MAD MAD MAD SPORTS WORLD
THE LITTLE BOOK OF CORPORATE LIES
RED HOT MONOGAMY
LOVE DAT CAT
HOW TO SURVIVE A JEWISH MOTHER

Retail $7.95
WHY MEN DON'T HAVE A CLUE
LADIES, START YOUR ENGINES!
ULI STEIN'S "ANIMAL LIFE"
ULI STEIN'S "I'VE GOT IT BUT IT'S JAMMED"
ULI STEIN'S "THAT SHOULD NEVER HAVE HAPPENED"

NO HANG-UPS – CASSETTES Retail $5.98
Vol. I: GENERAL MESSAGES (M or F)
Vol. II: BUSINESS MESSAGES (M or F)
Vol. III: 'R' RATED MESSAGES (M or F)
Vol. V: CELEBRI-TEASE